Songs
of
Freedom

By Bryan Marshall & David Marshall

Illustrated by Wil Clay

Published by Blue Sky Project, Inc.
First edition

Library of Congress Control Number: 2010904364
I.S.B.N: 9780578041124

Blue Sky Project, Inc. Blue Sky Project is a 501 c3 not-for-profit that supports social justice
initiatives that encourage all people to explore and discover the joys and challenges of living
in a free and open society. Blue Sky creates and distributes original film, video, print and other
media that are intended to inform, educate and inspire. Blue Sky projects are intended for broad
distribution through a wide range of venues that may include (but not limited to) classrooms,
television broadcast, film screenings, and internet; as well as community-based settings such as
museums, libraries and individual interest groups.

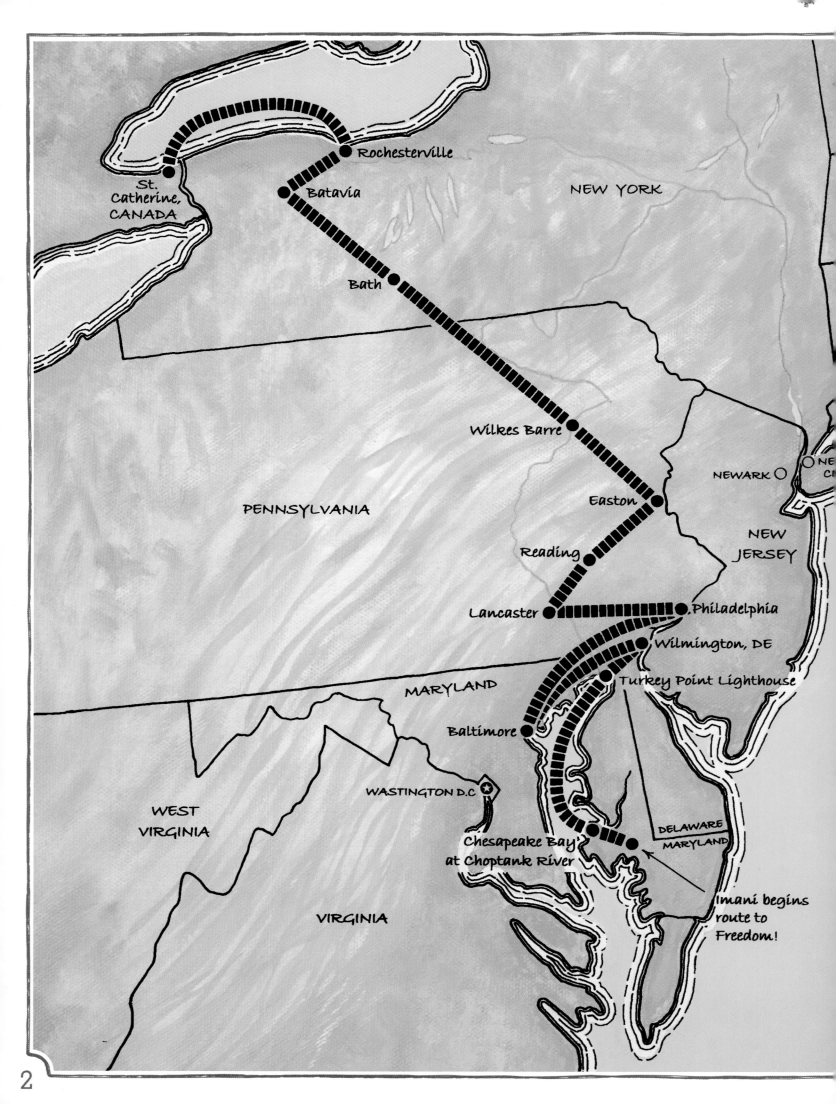

St. Catherine, CANADA

Rochesterville

Batavia

Bath

NEW YORK

PENNSYLVANIA

Wilkes Barre

NEWARK

NE
Cl

Easton

NEW JERSEY

Reading

Lancaster

Philadelphia

Wilmington, DE

Turkey Point Lighthouse

MARYLAND

Baltimore

WASTINGTON D.C

WEST VIRGINIA

DELAWARE

MARYLAND

Chesapeake Bay
at Choptank River

Imani begins
route to
Freedom!

VIRGINIA

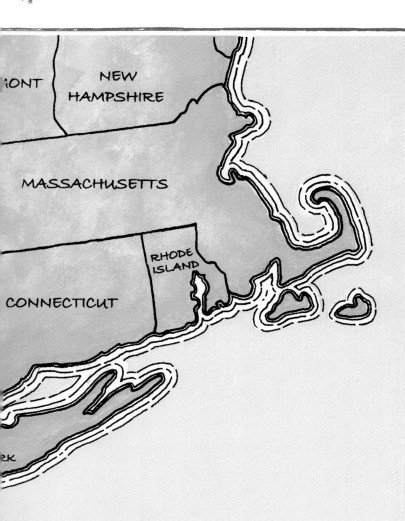

Mileages for Imani's Journey

Start	End	Miles
Plantation, MD	Choptank River, MD	8
Choptank River, MD	Turkey Point, MD	62
Turkey Point, MD	Wilmington, DE	35
Wilmington, DE	Baltimore, MD	74
Baltimore, MD	Philadelphia, PA	95
Philadelphia, PA	Lancaster, PA	67
Lancaster, PA	Reading, PA	30
Reading, PA	Easton, PA	47
Easton, PA	Wilkes Barre, PA	126
Wilkes Barre, PA	Bath, NY	99
Bath, NY	Batavia, NY	68
Batavia, NY	Rochester, NY	40
Rochester, NY	St. Catharines, ON	94

Total Journey: 845 miles

'We Raise de Wheat.

We raise de wheat,
Dey gib us de corn;
We bake de bread,
Dey gib us de crust;
We sif de meal,
Dey gib us de huss;
We peel de meat,
Dey gib us de skin;
And dat's de way
Dey take us in;

Mama named me Imani. She told me it means faith.
But the master, he named me Millie, because I am his slave.
I am nine years old. All of us slaves work for the Master.
The truth is, Master he beats us, sells us and works us until
we are dead. That is about all there is to slave living.

The sun is just coming up. Mama is washing clothes
at the big house. Papa is working in the fields.
I hear them singing as they pick out the old weeds.
The leaves are new green and smelling of summer.

At the Meeting Tree, Old Joseph tells me to sweep
the porch at the big house. "Keep clear of the Missus,"
he says. "She's meaner'n a scalded cat this mornin'."

Titus is the Master's hunting dog. I always give him a bite
of bread, and he licks my hand. He belongs to the Master
too, just like me.

One last porch corner and my work is done.
The broom just slips out of my hand, and bang,
it hits the floor. I hear a scream and look around
the corner. There is the Missus with her morning
coffee running all down her dress.

The Missus screams at Joseph, "Lock this creature in
the root cellar until it's sold at the next slave market.
Look what it's done."

9

'Master Going to Sell Us Tomorrow'

Mother, is Master goin'
to sell me tomorrow?
Yes, yes, yes. Oh,
watch and pray.

Goin' to sell me
in Baltimore?
Yes, yes, yes.
Oh, watch and pray...

What's that noise? They are coming to sell me! I'll never see Mama or Papa again. I want to run. But where can I go?

It is dark as the devil's night down here. I hum a song about the Master selling me south. I do not sing the words but I know they are there.

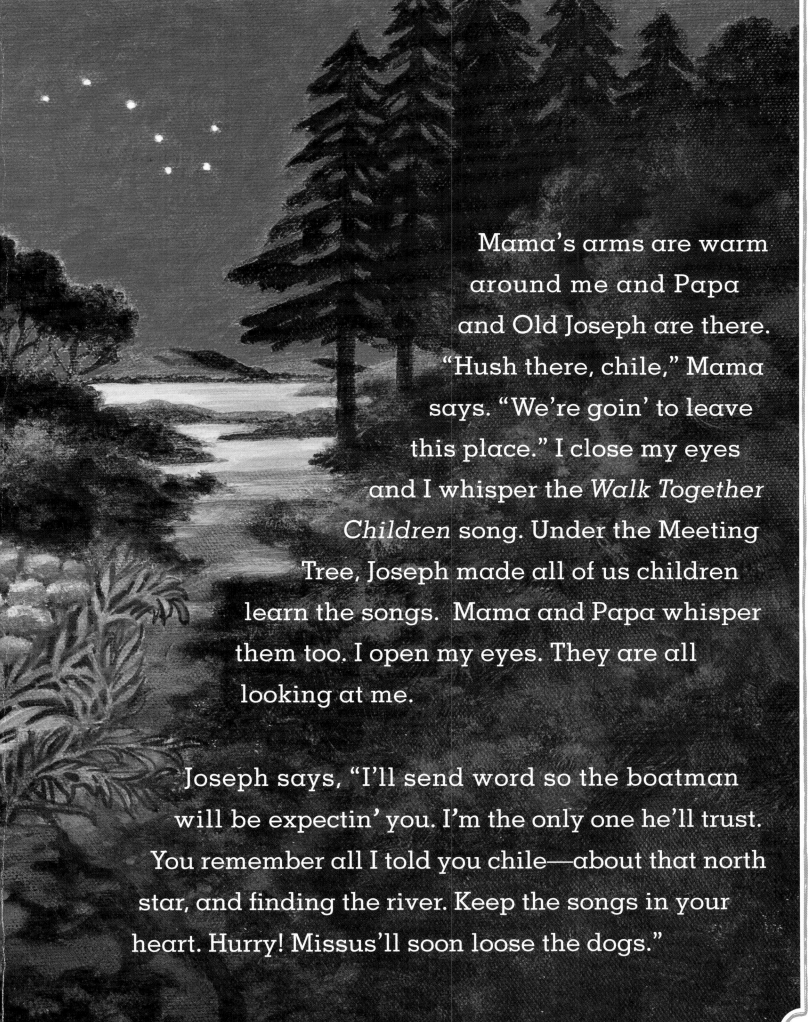

Mama's arms are warm around me and Papa and Old Joseph are there. "Hush there, chile," Mama says. "We're goin' to leave this place." I close my eyes and I whisper the *Walk Together Children* song. Under the Meeting Tree, Joseph made all of us children learn the songs. Mama and Papa whisper them too. I open my eyes. They are all looking at me.

Joseph says, "I'll send word so the boatman will be expectin' you. I'm the only one he'll trust. You remember all I told you chile—about that north star, and finding the river. Keep the songs in your heart. Hurry! Missus'll soon loose the dogs."

'Sweet Chariot'

Swing low, sweet chariot,
Coming for to carry me home
Swing low, sweet chariot,
Coming for to carry me home

I looked over Jordan, and what did I see
Coming for to carry me home?
A band of angels coming after me
Coming for to carry me home

If you get there before I do
Coming for to carry me home
Tell all my friends I'm coming too
Coming for to carry me home

I'm sometimes up, I'm sometimes down
Coming for to carry me home
But still my soul feels heavenly bound
Coming for to carry me home

We find the bay and walk all night in water, following the North Star. When dawn comes, we hide in the roots of a big old tree. Mama gives me corn mush to eat. She holds me until I am asleep. I wake up to dogs barking. Wheeee! The dogs are coming for us. Titus comes slobbering to my hand. I give him a lick of corn mush and he leaves us. I am cold and so tired. Mama sings quietly about a sweet chariot coming to carry me home.

We follow the star until a big river joins the bay. There is an old plank barn. I see a white cloth tied over the door. Papa says it looks bad. I tell Papa that Joseph said the white cloth means it is safe. Papa says to Mama, "We have one smart chile."

The next morning a man calls us awake. His face
is all lines and wrinkles. He gives Papa a bundle
of clothes. "Not safe here," he says. "Slave hunters
are comin'. Hide in my barn. There're others there."

Papa does not trust him but Mama says,
"He's a freed slave."

'Let My People Go'

The Lord told Moses
what to do
Let my people go
To lead the enslaved
children through
Let my people go

Let us all from
bondage flee
Let my people go
And let us all in
Christ be free
Let my people go

Chorus:
Go down, Moses
Way down in
Egypt's land
Tell ol' Pharoah
Let my people go.

I cannot see any other folk so I do not know the right of it. Under the straw, it is quiet until Mama starts humming. She does that when she is thinking about things. I start whispering the words to *Let My People Go* and soon there are others whispering. Like Sunday service but soft as wind. I snuggle close to Mama and my trembling stops.

When the sun is high in the sky, the wrinkle-face man brings corn bread and fish. "Time you be going to the boat," he says. Wheeee! Five black folk crawl out from under the straw. The boatman makes us hide until the boat leaves the land.

The boat rocks like it is trying to tip me out. Lord!
I hold on like I will never let go. Everyone is scared
until Mama tells me to sing *Wade In The Water*.
Soon everyone is singing with me, even Papa,
and he cannot sing.

♪ 'Wade In The Water'

Wade in the water
Wade in the water, children
Wade in the water
God's a-going to trouble the water

See that host all dressed in white
God's a-going to trouble the water
The leader looks like the Israelite
God's a-going to trouble the water

See that band all dressed in red
God's a-going to trouble the water
Looks like the band that Moses led
God's a-going to trouble the water

Look over yonder, what do you see?
God's a-going to trouble the water
The Holy Ghost a-coming on me
God's a-going to trouble the water

From the rocking and the smells of fish and tar and all,
I feel sick near to die. The others are still singing softly,
and we sail as quiet as the wind, night and day and
most of the next night.

23

"Turkey Point," the captain says and he points at a bright light on a tower. "Almost there."

A white man and a black woman called Harriet Tubman wait for us. She gives me shoes but they pinch my feet. I wonder if Freedom will be any better than plantation living!

I say, "Thank you, Missus." She has a gun in her belt. Papa says, "A black woman with a six-shooter! What next?"

Harriet Tubman says, "Sometimes you have to pay a high price for freedom."

Mama, Papa and me travel for days and nights
beyond counting. Sometimes on foot, but mostly
hidden in wagons. When will it end? How could
Freedom be so far? We stay in huts and houses and
pass through cities so big they make my head spin
with noise and smell. At Lucretia Mott's 'station' in
Philadelphia, we have to stay quiet for days until the
next 'shepherd' comes to take us to the promised land.
In Batavia we stay in a big old house and we get to
sing for a whole day, and it is not even Sunday!

♪ "Keep Your Lamp Trimmed and Burning"

Keep your lamps trimmed and burning,
Keep your lamps trimmed and burning,
Keep your lamps trimmed and burning,
The time is drawing nigh.

Children, don't get weary,
Children, don't get weary,
Children, don't get weary,
'Til your work is done.

Christian journey soon be over
Christian journey soon be over
Christian journey soon be over
The time is drawing nigh.

27

In Rochester a man with bushy hair and a big moustache named Frederick Douglass says he will write about me being a slave and all. He has his own newspaper and he dresses just like the Master. "Are we free yet Mister?" I ask.

"One more boat ride to go from Kelsey's Landing,"
he says, and he smiles kindly so I feel better. He talks
to my Papa, and Mama takes Papa's hand. I get right
between them and watch this Frederick Douglass.
He is not afraid of anything.

This boat is big with many black folk like me.
I see no land anyplace. I am trembling to be over
all that water and the boat is going so fast. Lord!

"Land-ho," calls a sailor next morning.
"Toronto off the port bow."

I hurry to be first to see Freedom. It looks so fine.

'Free At Last'

Free at last, free at last
I thank God I'm free at last.
Free at last, free at last
I thank God I'm free at last.

We have a house of our own. I am wearing shoes.
The trees are turned to bright colors and the
mornings smell of cold. I go to school.
I am learning to read and write. I do not have
to hide any more. Mama and Papa and I sing
whenever we are at home. Now, everyone calls
me Imani, my true name. I have found Freedom,
and I will never ever be a slave again.

Special thanks to our supporters
who made *Songs of Freedom* sing!

FUNDERS
Daisy Marquis Jones Foundation
Rochester Area Community Foundation
Eastman Kodak
Bausch & Lomb
New York State
Post-Central
Studios at Linden Oaks
Xerox
Canandaigua National Bank and Trust
Rochester Gas & Electric

HISTORY ADVISORS
Dr. Spencer Crew,
Clarence J. Robinson Professor of American,
African-American, and Public History
George Mason University

Dr. Kate Clifford Larson,
Historian and Harriet Tubman Scholar

EDUCATION PARTNERS
Rochester City School District
University of Rochester Warner School of Education
Rochester Freedom School
Genesee Country Museum
Rochester Museum & Science Center

Learn more about *Songs of Freedom* at SongsOfFreedom.net